There Is No I in TEAM

by Myka-Lynne Sokoloff
illustrated by Scott J. Wakefield

SCHOOL PUBLISHERS

Printed in China

ISBN 10: 0-15-351029-3
ISBN 13: 978-0-15-351029-8

Ordering Options
ISBN 10: 0-15-350602-4 (Grade 5 On-Level Collection)
ISBN 13: 978-0-15-350602-4 (Grade 5 On-Level Collection)
ISBN 10: 0-15-357954-4 (package of 5)
ISBN 13: 978-0-15-357954-7 (package of 5)

4 5 6 7 8 9 10   0940   12 11 10 09

CHARACTERS

COACH LIM

NARRATOR

EMILY

LUPE

ANDERS

WILLIAM

SOVANN

ANDREW

MAN AT CAR WASH

PRINCIPAL

SERVER IN
RESTAURANT

3

COACH: Welcome, Rockets. I'm looking forward to coaching our team again this season.

ROCKETS: Hi, Coach!

COACH: We'll start warming up in a few minutes. First, though, I want to share my thoughts on being part of a team. You each have an important role to play.

NARRATOR: The team members nudge one another and roll their eyes because they have heard this speech so many times before.

COACH: I'll tell you the ingredients for a winning team. One is practice. Another is discipline. The last one is teamwork. Without these three ingredients, in equal proportions, a team is inadequate. I want you all to work for the good of the team instead of trying to be a star yourself. Remember, there is no *I* in *TEAM*.

NARRATOR: The Rockets get to work practicing drills. In a few weeks, they are working well as a team. In fact, they win their first game.

COACH: I'm so pleased that you won. You all made me proud. Still, I was dismayed when I heard a couple of you showing off after the game. I'd like to see winners who are modest, not winners who brag about how great they are. Remember, there is no *I* in *TEAM*.

NARRATOR: The team members take the coach's words to heart. They behave respectfully on the court. They support each other off the court, as well. Then one day, Emily tells her friend Lupe that she is leaving the team.

EMILY: Lupe, I'm going to have to quit the team. My mother is very sick. My family needs me at home.

LUPE: Everyone will be so sorry to lose you. You are a great player.

5

NARRATOR: Lupe tells Coach Lim and the team about what Emily has said.

COACH: What grim news. We will be very sorry to lose Emily.

WILLIAM: Coach, I wish we could do something for Emily and her family.

ANDERS: I know a charity that helps people who are sick, like Emily's mom.

SOVANN: It would be nice if we could raise some money for that charity.

COACH: That's a great idea, kids! Any thoughts on how we can do that?

NARRATOR: The team members brainstorm some ideas. They decide to hold a car wash. Then on the day of the car wash the team members prepare.

COACH: Are you ready, Rockets?

WILLIAM: I've got the sponges.

LUPE: I've got towels.

ANDERS: I've got soap and water.

SOVANN: I have the hose, Coach.

COACH: Let's get started!

ANDREW: Good morning, sir. Would you like your car to sparkle like never before?

MAN: I would. You are talking to one disgruntled customer. You kids did a poor job washing my car last week. I'd like you to do it again, and it's crucial that you get it right this time. I don't plan to pay you either.

ANDREW: I'm sorry, sir. We weren't here last week. That must have been another group trying to raise money. We would be happy to wash your car. If you don't like the job we do, you won't need to pay us. How does that sound?

MAN: That sounds fair.

NARRATOR: The team gets to work on the man's car.

ANDREW: What do you think, sir?

MAN: I apologize for my behavior. I'm aghast that I blamed you. Your team did a wonderful job on my car. Here is a tip for you.

ANDREW: Thank you, but please don't fret, sir. It was an honest mistake. I could not take your tip. I'm just part of the team.

MAN: Please take it. Add it to the money you are raising.

NARRATOR: The car wash was a big success. The team raised a lot of money for the charity.

COACH: You all did a terrific job today at the car wash. Emily's family should be really pleased. I was especially proud of the way everyone pitched in today.

ROCKETS: There is no *I* in *CAR WASH*, Coach.

WILLIAM: Today was fun. Maybe we could hold another fund-raiser.

ANDY: Coach, I have an idea. We could bake things. Then we could sell them during halftime at our games.

NARRATOR: The team raises more money during the season and gives it all to the grateful charity.

NARRATOR: At the end of the season, the Rockets take part in the play-off games. Coach Lim's team comes in second for the season. At a sports dinner, the team is well-behaved. Team members clap for the season winners and listen quietly to the eminent speaker, the principal of the school.

PRINCIPAL: I am getting a bit absentminded. I must amend my statement that there was just one more award. Actually, I have two more special awards. The first one is a thank-you from a charity. One of our teams raised $350 and gave all of it away to help people who are sick. The second award is for the best teamwork. This award also goes to the same team, Coach Lim's Rockets. Congratulations on your fine work!

NARRATOR: Later that week, the team goes out for pizza to celebrate their season.

KELLY: Hello. I'm Kelly. I'll be your server. Do you know what you would like to order?

TEAM MEMBERS: We want pizza!

KELLY: What do you want on the pizza?

LUPE: Coach, do we have to agree on what we want on our pizza?

COACH: You have worked so well as a team all along. I think we can rest assured that it won't be difficult for you to agree on what you want.

LUPE: I'm envisioning a pizza covered in pepperoni.

ANDERS: Mmm, but mushrooms are irresistible.

ANDREW: I want olives.

SOVANN: I want peppers.

WILLIAM: I want extra cheese.

WAITRESS: That's quite a concoction. Do you want all those things on the same pizza?

ANDERS: I don't like peppers. I want a separate pizza, please.

COACH: I want, I want, I want. It sounds like you all want something different. Why does ordering a pizza have to turn into such a crisis? What happened to teamwork?

LUPE: There is no *I* in *TEAM*, Coach . . .

WILLIAM: . . . but there is an *I* in PIZZA!

Think Critically

1. Look at the chart on page 10. Which baked good is most expensive? Which is least expensive?

2. What questions did you have that were answered as you read the play?

3. Why did the Rockets decide to have a car wash?

4. Explain the meaning of the expression "There is no *I* in *TEAM*."

5. What are some other ways that members of a team can work together? Explain your answer.

 Science

Soap Bubbles You need soap and water to clean a dirty car. Do research at the library or on the Internet to learn how soap bubbles form. Report your findings on a poster.

School-Home Connection Ask family members to share experiences they have had working with a team of other people or helping others.

Word Count: 1,053